RICHARDS MEMORIAL LIBRARY
18 NORTH WASHINGTON STREE
NORTH ATTLEBORO, MA 02760

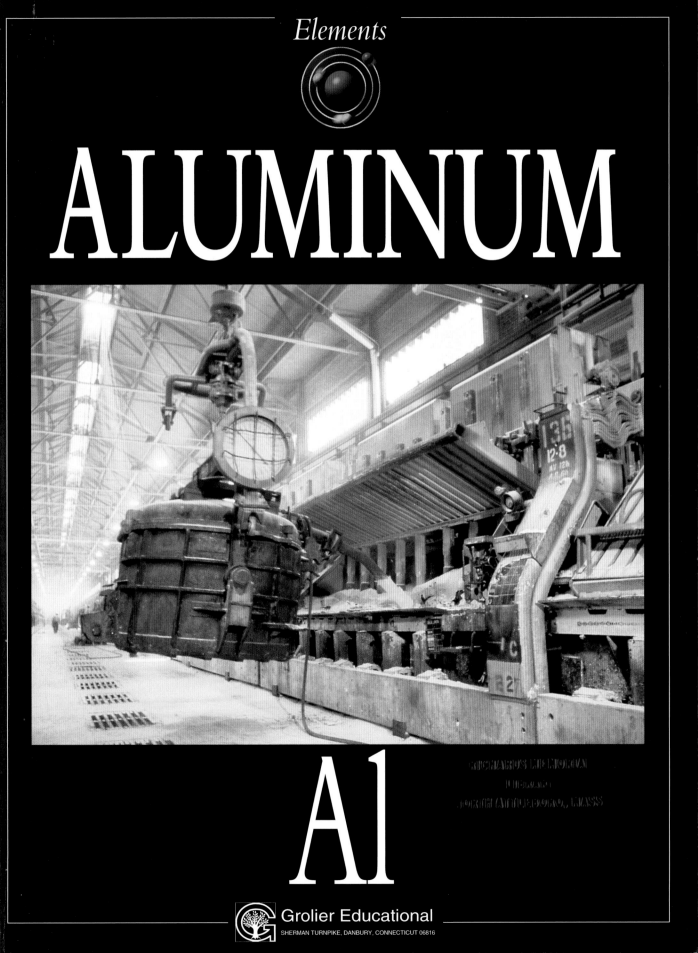

Elements

ALUMINUM

Al

Grolier Educational

SHERMAN TURNPIKE, DANBURY, CONNECTICUT 06816

How to use this book

This book has been carefully developed to help you understand the chemistry of the elements. In it you will find a systematic and comprehensive coverage of the basic qualities of each element. Each two-page entry contains information at various levels of technical content and language, along with definitions of useful technical terms, as shown in the thumbnail diagram to the right. There is a comprehensive glossary of technical terms at the back of the book, along with an extensive index, key facts, an explanation of the periodic table, and a description of how to interpret chemical equations.

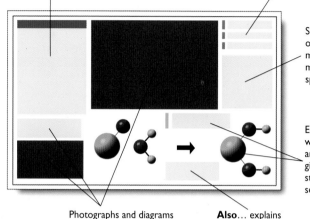

The main text follows the sequence of information in the book and summarizes the concepts presented on the two pages.

Technical definitions.

Substatements flesh out the ideas in the main text with more fact and specific explanation.

Equations are written as symbols and sometimes given as "ball-and-stick" diagrams – see page 48.

Photographs and diagrams have been carefully selected and annotated for clarity.

Also... explains advanced concepts.

Author
Brian Knapp, BSc, PhD
Project consultant
Keith B. Walshaw, MA, BSc, DPhil
　　　(Head of Chemistry, Leighton Park School)
Industrial consultant
Jack Brettle, BSc, PhD (Chief Research Scientist, Pilkington plc)
Art Director
Duncan McCrae, BSc
Editor
Elizabeth Walker, BA
Special photography
Ian Gledhill
Illustrations
David Woodroffe
Electronic page makeup
Julie James Graphic Design
Designed and produced by
EARTHSCAPE EDITIONS
Print consultants
Landmark Production Consultants Ltd
Reproduced by
Leo Reprographics
Printed and bound by
Paramount Printing Company Ltd

First published in the United States in 1996 by Grolier Educational, Sherman Turnpike, Danbury, CT 06816

Copyright © 1996
Atlantic Europe Publishing Company Limited

Cataloguing information may be obtained directly from Grolier Educational.

Set ISBN 0–7172–7572–8
Volume ISBN 0–7172–7579–5
Library of Congress Number: 95–082222

All rights reserved. No part of this publication may be reproduced, stored in a retrieval system, or transmitted in any form or by any means, electronic, mechanical, photocopying, recording or otherwise, without permission in writing of the publisher.

Acknowledgments
The publishers would like to thank the following for their kind help and advice: Alcan International, British Alcan Aluminium plc, Kjc Operating Company, Dr Angus W. R. McCrae, Rolls-Royce plc, Frank Sperling and Pippa Trounce.

Picture credits
All photographs are from the **Earthscape Editions** photolibrary except the following:
(c=center t=top b=bottom l=left r=right)
courtesy of **British Alcan Aluminium plc** BACK COVER, 4/5c, 10b, 10/11t, 12t, 12b, 13t, 13b, 18bl, 19t, 20bl; **Alcan International** 1, 16b, 43t, 44bl, 44/45b, 45tr; courtesy of **Chubb Security Group** 39tr; courtesy of **Rolls-Royce plc** BACK COVER, 20/21t, 23tr; by permission of **NASA** 30bl and **ZEFA** 41b, 42/43b.

Front cover: Aluminum can be extruded in one piece to make thin forms that can be torn easily, such as soda cans. The ruby in the background is aluminium oxide.
Title page: Molten aluminum being poured from a crucible into a holding furnace.

This product is manufactured from sustainable managed forests. For every tree cut down at least one more is planted.

The demonstrations described or illustrated in this book are not for replication. The Publisher cannot accept any responsibility for any accidents or injuries that may result from conducting the experiments described or illustrated in this book.

Contents

Introduction

An element is a substance that cannot be broken down into a simpler substance by any known means. Each of the 92 naturally occurring elements is therefore one of the fundamental materials from which everything in the Universe is made. This book is about aluminum.

Aluminum

Aluminum, the third most common element on Earth after oxygen and silicon, and by far the most abundant metal on Earth, is now used very widely for everything from soft-drink cans to car bodies to window frames. Compounds containing aluminum are found in materials as different as antacid medicines, the insulation materials in our homes and in the small white flecks (called vermiculite) in garden composts.

Aluminum is one of a number of soft and weak metals (like copper and tin) that scientists call "poor" metals. But aluminum alloys, mixtures of aluminum and other metals, produce materials as tough as steel.

The name aluminum comes from the word *alumen*, which is the Latin name for alum. Alum is an age-old material called a mordant, used for making dyes stick to fabrics.

Although it is so widely used today, aluminum has only recently come into use. This is because aluminum is so strongly attracted to oxygen that it can only be refined using huge amounts of electrical energy and electricity did not become readily available until this century.

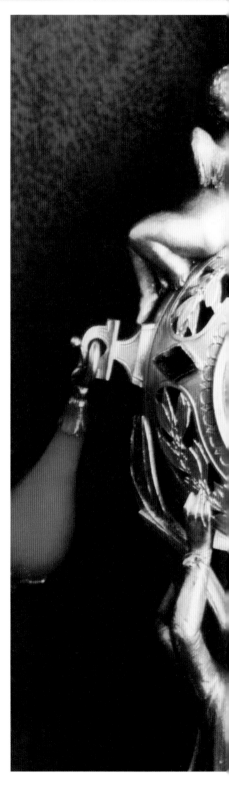

Thus it is sometimes known as the metal of the 20th century, just as iron was the metal of the 19th century.

Although electricity is relatively more plentiful and less expensive than it used to be, refining aluminum from its ore is still a costly process. This is why aluminum is often recycled. This way we do not have to "waste" energy refining more of the metal than we need to.

◀ For centuries aluminum could not easily be refined. This made it more precious than gold or silver! For much of the 19th century some important and wealthy people even used plates of aluminum in preference to fine china or silver.

For the same reason aluminum was used in settings that contained precious stones. The object shown here belonged to Napoleon III of France (b.1808–d.1873).

▶ Aluminum can now be isolated from its ores relatively cheaply and has many everyday applications.

Minerals containing aluminum

Aluminum is one of the most common elements in the rocks of the Earth's surface, yet it is very rarely seen as the shiny metal we are used to seeing as soft-drink cans, etc. This is because aluminum easily combines with silicon and oxygen to make clay, the stuff of soils.

Micas

Micas are minerals made of sheets of aluminum, silicon and oxygen (known as aluminosilicates). Stacks of these sheets are connected together by metal ions; potassium and magnesium are among the most common.

The way the sheets are connected too is very important because it gives the minerals many of their properties. Sheet silicates all break up into thin flakes. For this reason, several of the sheet silicates are used as lubricants; for example, talcum powder is made from the mineral talc.

Mica is easily recognized as a silicate because it peels away into thin, almost transparent sheets. The main varieties are biotite, which is black, and muscovite, which is brown.

▶ Muscovite, a brown form of mica.

▶ Feldspar crystals are opaque and either pink or white. You can see them clearly in this granite sample.

Feldspar

Feldspars are common silicate minerals and found in most igneous rocks. To form an aluminum silicate of this kind, some of the oxygen atoms found in silica are replaced by aluminum atoms together with a small proportion of atoms of the metals potassium, sodium or calcium. Variety in the color of feldspars is influenced by the proportions of these metals. For example, potassium feldspar is pale pink, whereas calcium feldspar is white.

Corundum

Corundum is a very hard, brown to black mineral, next only to diamond in its hardness. It is an aluminum oxide and is found next to where granite and other volcanic rocks occur. The material we call emery is made from corundum. Emery cloth is a common abrasive cloth, while emery powder is glued onto disks to make cutting and sanding tools.

► Aluminum sulfate (commonly known as alum).

clay: a microscopically small platelike mineral that makes up the bulk of many soils. It has a sticky feel when wet.

crystal: a substance that has grown freely so that it can develop external faces. Compare with crystalline, where the atoms were not free to form individual crystals and amorphous, where the atoms are arranged irregularly.

granite: an igneous rock with a high proportion of silica (usually over 65%). It has well-developed large crystals. The largest pink, gray or white crystals are of feldspar.

igneous rock: a rock that has solidified from molten rock, either volcanic lava on the Earth's surface or molten magma deep underground. In either case the rock develops a network of interlocking crystals.

Kaolinite

Kaolinite is a clay mineral found in many of the world's soils. It is composed of sheets containing aluminum silicates. Kaolinite is a soft mineral whose crystals are too small to be seen even with an ordinary microscope.

Water molecules can be absorbed between the silicate sheets, which explains why soils shrink and swell with wetting and drying.

Kaolinite is mined as china clay and used for porcelain, pottery, the filler in drug tablets, and also to make smooth-textured paper.

Also...

The chemical formula for corundum is Al_2O_3 (aluminum oxide). There are three main types of feldspar, varying only in the metal that bonds the sheets together. The chemical formula for these feldspars is $KAlSi_3O_8$ (potassium feldspar), $CaAlSi_3O_8$ (calcium feldspar) and $NaAlSi_3O_8$ (sodium feldspar). The chemical formula for muscovite mica is $KAl_2(Si_3Al)O_{10}(OH)_2$ (potassium aluminosilicate).

▼ The structure of many sheet minerals containing aluminum. Mica and kaolinite are good examples.

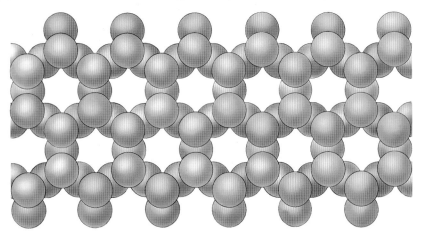

Gemstones containing aluminum

Whereas clay is made of tiny, unremarkable crystal plates that are too small to see without a powerful microscope, just occasionally, usually near where volcanoes have been active, aluminum combines with other elements to form some of the world's most remarkable crystals. These are gemstones such as sapphire and ruby.

Ruby

Ruby is a deep red crystal, one of the most prized of all gemstones. It is made mainly of aluminum and oxygen (aluminum oxide). This mineral, known as corundum, is transparent. But when it occurs with small amounts of another element, chromium, the color changes to something between pale rose and deep red.

The world's best rubies come from Myanmar (Burma), where they have been naturally weathered from rocks and washed by rivers to accumulate among river gravels.

Small rubies can now be made artificially, and these are routinely used in many of the world's lasers.

◄ Beryl is made from aluminum, beryllium, silicon and oxygen. In its pure form it makes emerald, a deep-green transparent gemstone, and a paler version called aquamarine.

Beryl forms six-sided crystals, making the mineral crystals easy to identify. It is often found associated with volcanic rocks.

Emeralds are found where volcanic activity has altered limestones, often in the form of very large crystals. One of the largest crystals found weighed 200 tons! Needless to say, this was not of the transparent gemstone variety.

▼ Ruby set in the greenstone rock (zoisite) in which it is normally found. The hexagonal crystal system to which ruby belongs shows clearly in this example.

Ruby

bond: chemical bonding is either a transfer or sharing of electrons by two or more atoms. There are a number of types of chemical bond, some very strong (such as covalent bonds), others weak (such as hydrogen bonds). Chemical bonds form because the linked molecule is more stable than the unlinked atoms from which it formed. For example, the hydrogen molecule (H_2) is more stable than single atoms of hydrogen, which is why hydrogen gas is always found as molecules of two hydrogen atoms.

gemstones: a wide range of minerals valued by people, both as crystals (such as emerald) and as decorative stones (such as agate). There is no single chemical formula for a gemstone.

molecule: a group of two or more atoms held together by chemical bonds.

▼►► Sapphire is a pale-blue to deep-violet form of corundum (see also page 6). The colors are produced by various amounts of the elements iron and titanium.
Most transparent corundum is known as sapphire, except for the red varieties, which are called ruby (see page 8). Consequently, rubies and sapphires are often collected from the same deposits as the corundum that is used in industry. Sapphires can be made artificially and are used where hard wearing is vital, such as for the jewels of watch bearings. Sapphire can also be used as an abrasive.

Bauxite

Aluminum is found in every handful of soil you hold. It begins as a part of minerals in rocks such as granite. One of the most common minerals containing aluminum is pink or gray feldspar. To break down the feldspar and make clay, all that nature requires is water, warm weather and a very long period of time.

As rainwater washes over the surface of the feldspar, invisible chemical reactions occur. They are the same reactions that cause limestone statues on buildings to become weathered. The water, often with carbon dioxide gas from the air, rots the feldspar. The result is to release the elements in the feldspar and put them into solution. The aluminum quickly combines with silicon and oxygen to form clay. Because the clay is formed in water, it can no longer be destroyed by future rainfall. This is the secret of how aluminum is locked up in the world's clays and why it is so difficult to recover it.

The ore containing aluminum, called bauxite, forms in places where the aluminum compounds become especially concentrated.

◀▲ Open-pit mining of bauxite in Jamaica. The waste rock and soil, called the overburden, is first removed, and then the soft bauxite is dug out in large slices before being carried away using dumptrucks. The overburden is used to fill in the areas already mined of its bauxite. The land can then be reclaimed.

feldspar: a mineral consisting of sheets of aluminum silicate. This is the mineral from which the clay in soils is made.

granite: an igneous rock with a high proportion of silica (usually over 65%). It has well-developed large crystals. The largest pink, gray or white crystals are of feldspar.

ore: a rock containing enough of a useful substance to make mining it worthwhile.

Bauxite

The name bauxite comes from an ancient mine site at Les Baux in the south of France. Bauxite is a tropical soil material, full of clay like any other soil. Under hot, moist conditions some of the aluminum does not get locked up as clay but instead forms sheets of aluminum oxide.

Aluminum oxide is usually colorless or grayish-white, and often forms alongside oxides of iron under humid tropical conditions. Iron oxides are red, and their bright color masks the pale aluminum oxide. Most bauxite is found inside the tropical red (iron-containing) subsoil material known as laterite.

To get aluminum metal from bauxite the aluminum must be separated from both the oxygen and the oxides of iron.

Modern bauxite mines are located where the ores contain at least half their volume of aluminum oxide. All of the ores are soil layers, and thus are always mined in shallow open-cut pits. Today the majority of bauxite comes from Guinea, Australia, Jamaica and Brazil.

The known reserves of bauxite will last for several hundred years if the consumption can be kept to present levels by careful recycling.

◀ Bauxite rock has an orange-red color because of staining by iron oxides.

The process of manufacturing aluminum metal from bauxite has many stages. These are described here and on the following pages.

The aluminum industry begins

The history of the aluminum industry is quite short. The industrial method for separating aluminum from bauxite ore was only discovered in 1854, and the first aluminum was produced in 1859. But it is now one of the most important metal industries in the world.

How aluminum came to be refined

The aluminum industry had to wait for the development of electricity. In fact, the person who first separated aluminum from its ore was Danish professor Hans Christian Oersted, one of the pioneers of electricity.

However, only after discoveries in 1886 by Charles Martin Hall of Ohio, Paul L. T. Héroult of France, and in 1888 by Karl Joseph Bayer of Germany, did it become possible to refine large amounts of aluminum. Even then, large-scale processing did not get under way until the early part of the 20th century. This is because relatively cheap electricity supplies were needed, and it took some time for the power-generating industry to build generators large enough for the needs of an aluminum refinery. So, while iron was the metal of the 19th century, aluminum became the metal of the 20th century.

◄▲ In 1886 Charles Martin Hall (above) of the United States and Paul L. T. Héroult (below left) of France discovered a way to dissolve alumina in molten cryolite and so make aluminum commercially. For this reason the process is called the Hall–Héroult process, and it is still in use today.

refining: separating a mixture into the simpler substances of which it is made. In the case of a rock, it means the extraction of the metal that is mixed up in the rock. In the case of oil it means separating the fractions of which it is made.

◄ In this aluminum smelter (in Lochaber, Scotland) the power is provided by an on-site hydroelectric power plant. You can see the pipes that carry water to the power station turbines behind the main plant. It takes about 20 kilowatt-hours of electricity to produce a kilogram of aluminum.

▼ Because of the low percentage of aluminum in the bauxite ore from which it is extracted, large machines with bucket scoops have to be used to gain economies of scale.

This bauxite from Ghana is awaiting processing into alumina.

Dissolving aluminum compounds

Aluminum is a reactive metal. When exposed to the air, it immediately develops an oxide coating that prevents further corrosion. However, along with a few other metals, aluminum compounds can be dissolved by both acids and alkalis. Metal compounds with this special property are called amphoteric metals. This property has been exploited in the aluminum industry as a way of dissolving the aluminum compounds from bauxite while leaving the rest of the ore as a solid. This process, called the Bayer process, is shown on pages 16 and 17.

❶▲ The completely intact aluminum container used in the demonstration.

❷▶ Sodium hydroxide is poured into the container. It immediately begins to fizz and bubble.

amphoteric: a metal that will react with both acids and alkalis.

bauxite: an ore of aluminum, of which about half is aluminum oxide.

dissolve: to break down a substance in a solution without reacting.

solution: a mixture of a liquid and at least one other substance. Mixtures can be separated by physical means, for example, by evaporation and cooling.

❸◀ Underneath the bubbling a chemical reaction is taking place that is putting the aluminum into solution.

❹▼ The aluminum container after reaction. Notice that the container no longer has a bottom! The reaction time from start to finish was five minutes.

Also:

If sodium hydroxide (caustic soda – a powerful base) is poured into an aluminum saucepan, a chemical reaction will occur that dissolves the aluminum. Cleaning aluminum cookware with caustic soda is therefore not to be recommended!

EQUATION: Dissolving aluminum in sodium hydroxide

Aluminum + sodium hydroxide+ water ⇨ sodium aluminate + hydrogen

$$2Al(s) + 2NaOH(aq) + 6H_2O(l) \Rightarrow 2NaAl(OH)_4(aq) + 3H_2(g)$$

Concentrating bauxite ore

Bauxite is a red rocklike material. It consists of aluminum oxide and a wide range of unwanted substances. To produce aluminum metal, the ore first has to be concentrated, thus removing the bulk of the impurities. Then it goes to a refinery, where the pure metal is produced. The concentrating stage is called the Bayer process.

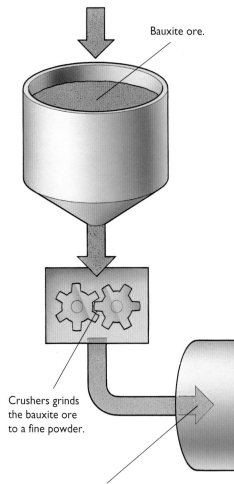

Bauxite ore.

Crushers grinds the bauxite ore to a fine powder.

The pulverized bauxite is mixed with sodium hydroxide (NaOH) at high pressure and temperature.

The Bayer process

Chemical reactions work most efficiently if the reactants have a large surface area. In the case of an ore, chemical reactions are made faster by pulverizing the ore into a powder. Bauxite powder is mixed with crushed sodium hydroxide (soda ash) and calcium oxide (lime) and then mixed with water.

The chemical reaction takes place at high temperatures and pressures, making the aluminum oxide soluble (as sodium aluminate), so that it can be drained off into settling tanks. Here, any solids, such as pieces of sand and iron oxide, settle out. The alumina is a light-brown liquid.

This liquid is drawn off and pumped into tall vats where it is allowed to cool. Inside the vats the liquid is stirred and tiny crystals of alumina form. The stirring causes the crystals to stick to each other until they are about the size of grains of sugar, then they sink to the bottom. The crystals are taken away and washed clear of any remaining liquid. They are then heat-dried, and the resulting alumina is a gray powder.

EQUATION: Production of alumina

(i) dissolving bauxite in sodium hydroxide

Bauxite + sodium hydroxide + water ⇨ sodium aluminate

$Al_2O_3(ore) + 2NaOH(aq) + 3H_2O ⇨ 2NaAl(OH)_4(aq) +$ impurities
                                                              red mud

(ii) recovering the sodium hydroxide to leave alumina

Sodium aluminate ⇨ alumina + sodium hydroxide

$2NaAl(OH)_4(aq) ⇨ Al_2O_3{\cdot}3H_2O(s) + 2NaOH(aq)$

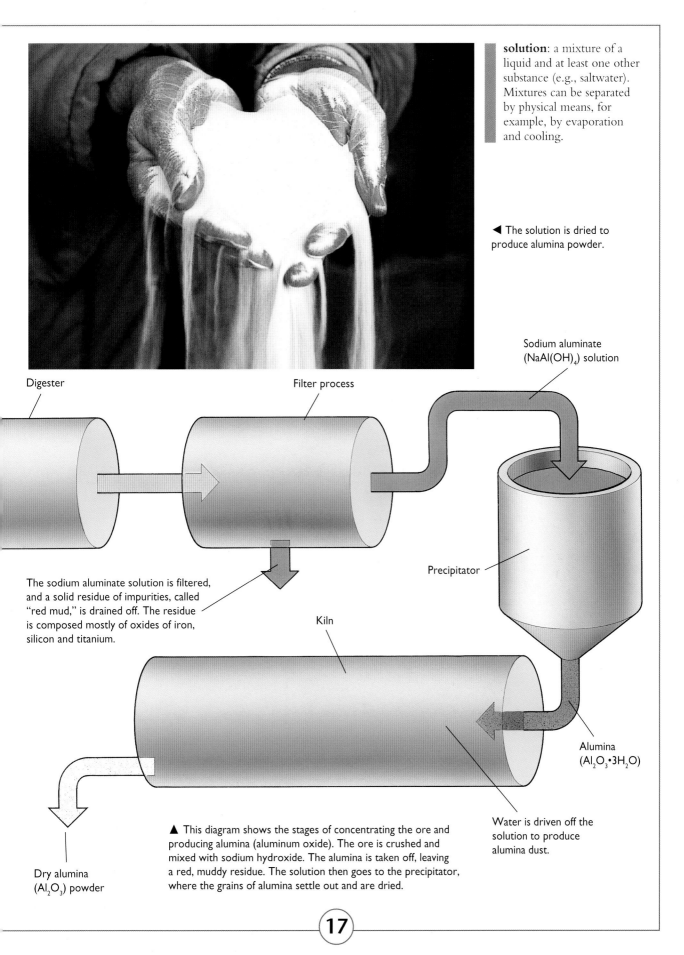

solution: a mixture of a liquid and at least one other substance (e.g., saltwater). Mixtures can be separated by physical means, for example, by evaporation and cooling.

◀ The solution is dried to produce alumina powder.

Sodium aluminate (NaAl(OH)$_4$) solution

Digester

Filter process

Precipitator

The sodium aluminate solution is filtered, and a solid residue of impurities, called "red mud," is drained off. The residue is composed mostly of oxides of iron, silicon and titanium.

Kiln

Alumina (Al$_2$O$_3$•3H$_2$O)

Water is driven off the solution to produce alumina dust.

▲ This diagram shows the stages of concentrating the ore and producing alumina (aluminum oxide). The ore is crushed and mixed with sodium hydroxide. The alumina is taken off, leaving a red, muddy residue. The solution then goes to the precipitator, where the grains of alumina settle out and are dried.

Dry alumina (Al$_2$O$_3$) powder

Aluminum refining

The partly purified ore of bauxite, called alumina, is still a compound of aluminum and oxygen. To refine this to aluminum, the alumina has to be dissolved and the aluminum recovered by electrical means.

The process of using electricity to separate a metal from its rock ore is called electrolysis and takes place inside electrolytic cells. The alumina has to be liquefied so that the aluminum compound will dissociate (break apart) into electrically charged particles called ions. Aluminum ions have a positive charge and can move through a solution to gather at the negatively charged electrode of the cell (the cathode).

Each cell uses a mere four to six volts, about the same as a dry cell used for a flashlight. But the current that flows is sometimes as much as 150,000 amps (equivalent to the maximum consumption of 300 households with all their appliances in use).

An aluminum smelter

Processing alumina happens on a large scale, but the electrical process cannot be done in a single large vat. Instead hundreds or even thousands of cells are used, made of steel with a carbon lining.

The process turns aluminum oxide into aluminum by removing the oxygen. This is called reduction.

The cells are first filled with a material called cryolite, which is heated to 980°C. Alumina will melt at a lower temperature when mixed with cryolite than if it were melted on its own. This saves electricity.

The alumina and cryolite mixture is then poured into the cell and rows of carbon electrodes are dipped into it. A current flows from the hanging electrodes to the carbon lining of the cell. At the bottom of the cells, embedded in the carbon lining, are collector plates (cathodes).

The electrical energy separates the aluminum ions from the oxygen ions and the aluminum collects on the plates at the bottom of the cell.

This process operates continuously, the molten aluminum being siphoned out of the cells and new alumina added from above. The aluminum can then be fed to mills and rolled into sheets, poured into molds where it cools to make ingots for later use, or mixed with other metals to make alloys.

◀ This is the "cell room" of an aluminum smelting plant. Each cell is up to ten by four meters. Each cell makes about nine hundred kilograms of aluminum each day

electrolysis: an electrical-chemical process that uses an electric current to cause the breakup of a compound and the movement of metal ions in a solution. The process happens in many natural situations (as for example in rusting) and is also commonly used in industry for purifying (refining) metals or for plating metal objects with a fine, even metal coating.

ion: an atom, or group of atoms, that has gained or lost one or more electrons and so developed an electrical charge. Ions behave differently from electrically neutral atoms and molecules. They can move in an electric field, and they can also bind strongly to solvent molecules such as water. Positively charged ions are called cations; negatively charged ions are called anions. Ions carry electrical current through solutions.

reduction: the removal of oxygen from a substance.

▲ Aluminum is being poured into molds to make ingots.

EQUATION: Overall equations for the reduction of alumina to aluminum

Alumina ⇨ aluminum + oxygen

$$2Al_2O_3(s) \quad \Rightarrow \quad 4Al(s) \quad + \quad 3O_2(g)$$

Carbon + oxygen ⇨ carbon dioxide

$$3C(s) \quad + \quad 3O_2(g) \quad \Rightarrow \quad 3CO_2(g)$$

▼ The alumina smelter where an electrolysis process separates the aluminum from the oxide electrically, using the Hall-Héroult process.

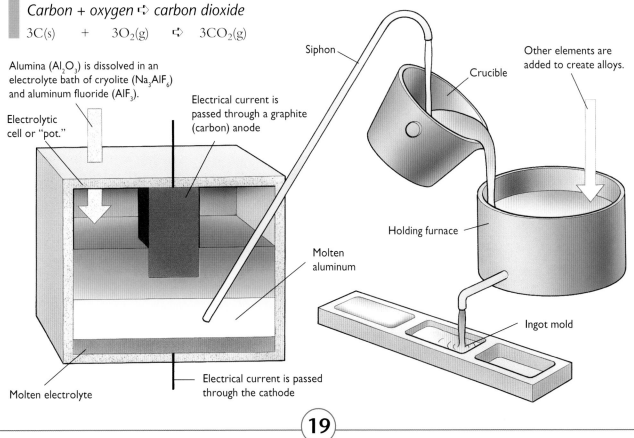

Alumina (Al_2O_3) is dissolved in an electrolyte bath of cryolite (Na_3AlF_6) and aluminum fluoride (AlF_3).

Electrolytic cell or "pot."

Electrical current is passed through a graphite (carbon) anode

Siphon

Crucible

Other elements are added to create alloys.

Holding furnace

Molten aluminum

Ingot mold

Molten electrolyte

Electrical current is passed through the cathode

The properties of aluminum

Aluminum is soft and easy to shape but will become harder if it is cold-worked by, for example, hammering or pressing. This is called annealing.

The other important property of aluminum is that it can be welded, using a very high temperature source such as an arc-welding machine and a stick of aluminum. Aluminum can also be brazed (high temperature soldering using a rod of brass) or soldered with other metals (although the soldered joints suffer corrosion, making them unsuited for some uses). Aluminum can also be made harder when formed as an alloy.

◀ Aluminum is being extruded (pushed through a press containing a specially shaped die) to create the intricate shapes needed for the building industry. This is siding.

▼ Aluminum alloys are widely used in aircraft parts, from the fuselage to the engines. Light weight and resistance to corrosion are important factors.

brazing: a form of soldering in which brass is used as the joining metal.

soldering: joining together two pieces of metal using solder, an alloy with a low melting point.

welding: fusing two pieces of metal together using heat.

▼ Aluminum foil, thin sheets that are readily used for packaging.

◄ Lightweight coin from China.

Saving weight and fuel with aluminum

Aluminum is one of the lightest metals. This means that it will take less energy to move a piece of aluminum than, for example, a piece of steel of the same size. The saving in weight, and so in energy, is especially important in transportation. If a steel container can be replaced by an aluminum alloy container, less fuel is needed to carry it, making the container cheaper to move.

The same is true of all the components of a vehicle. The engine block, the drive shafts, the radiator, the wheels and the body panels can all be made of aluminum alloys. The car thus weighs less, and the fuel consumption improves. Unfortunately, the price also increases, which is why many vehicles are still made of steel.

Aluminum alloys

Pure aluminum is easy to bend and form into shape, but it is not very strong. An alloy is a mixture of various elements designed to give the alloy special characteristics that pure metals do not have.

Common alloys

Normal refining processes do not remove all impurities from aluminum, so most commonly used industrial aluminum already has small amounts of iron, silicon and copper alloyed with it. Fortunately, alloying elements make aluminum stronger, but it remains easy to bend into shape.

The most common alloy of aluminum contains copper, magnesium, manganese, chromium, silicon, iron, nickel and zinc. Here silicon makes the aluminum flow better into casts of complicated shapes. Copper, on the other hand, makes the aluminum stronger. Adding 1.25% manganese makes the alloy exceptionally resistant to corrosion.

In all cases, the proportion of added elements is less than 10% of the final alloy; and because silicon mixes quite poorly in an alloy, no more than about 1.5% can be used.

Modern aircraft engine makers and power-station-turbine makers are working with new alloys that contain titanium or nickel to make lightweight aluminum even tougher.

Alloys that are forced into new shapes

For many purposes the aluminum alloy needs to be forced into a new shape, for example, made into a tube or pressed into a car body panel. The best alloys for this have a slightly different composition from those used for casting. These alloys get stronger and harder as they are worked, often at high temperatures.

▲ Not all alloys make strong materials. Mercury, for example, forms an amalgam with aluminum on contact, forming a liquid metal. The holes in this sample of aluminum show where the mercury has "eaten" its way through the sheet.

alloy: a mixture of a metal and various other elements.

corrosion: the *slow* decay of a substance resulting from contact with gases and liquids in the environment. The term is often applied to metals. Rust is the corrosion of iron.

▲ Aluminum alloys are commonly used for racing bicycles to give strength and light weight.

▼ Wind turbines, such as those shown below, are often made with aluminum alloys so that the blade weight is kept to a minimum. In exposed locations, resistance to corrosion is also vital.

▲ Aluminum is often found in electric motors. It is also widely used for the pistons in engines.

Special alloys

Aluminum alloys can be made as strong as steel. To make duralumin, which is both hard and strong, an alloy containing 4.5% copper, 0.6% manganese and 1.5% magnesium is heated to about 495°C and then dipped in cold water. It is then left to "age" over the next few days, during which time it beomes extremely hard.

To make alclad, an alloy that has a soft aluminum center and a hard, corrosion-resistant skin, an alloy of magnesium, zinc, copper and chromium is heat-treated, quenched and allowed to "age." It is an ideal material for use on aircraft fuselages.

Where the aluminum alloy needs to retain strength at very high temperatures, nickel is alloyed with aluminum.

Making use of the reactivity of aluminum

Aluminum is the most reactive metal in common use. All metals more reactive than aluminum (calcium, sodium, etc.) are unstable and need special handling.

The reactivity of aluminum has advantages and disadvantages. One advantage is that it readily reacts with oxygen from the air, forming a gastight and invisible oxide layer on its surface that protects the metal from environmental corrosion.

On the other hand, being so reactive, the metal is very difficult to separate from its ore, and the costs of manufacture are high.

Aluminum and the reactivity series

Each metal reacts with the environment differently. Some, like potassium, are highly reactive; others, like gold, are very stable.

When two different metals are placed in a conducting solution (an electrolyte such as salt water), a natural battery is formed. In a battery, one of the electrodes (the anode) always corrodes, while the other (the cathode) becomes plated (or coated) with material from the corroding electrode.

Which electrode corrodes, and which is protected (becomes plated) depends on the positions of the metals in the reactivity series. Metals above those in the table become corroded; those lower down are protected.

Aluminum is more reactive than, for example, iron, so when aluminum and iron are placed together in salt water, for example, the aluminum will corrode rather than the iron (see opposite).

The reactivity table also helps to explain why aluminum is so difficult to extract from its ores compared with many other common metals. The higher up the table, the more energy it takes to separate the metal from its ores. For example, iron (in the middle of the table) can be smelted (a chemcial reaction involving heat and a reducing agent) whereas aluminum (near the top of the table) can only be refined using large amounts of electrical energy.

REACTIVITY SERIES	
Element	Reactivity
potassium	*most reactive*
sodium	
calcium	
magnesium	
aluminum	
manganese	
chromium	
zinc	
iron	
cadmium	
tin	
lead	
copper	
mercury	
silver	
gold	
platinum	*least reactive*

Aluminum as a sacrificial anode

Aluminum is bolted onto the keels of many ships to protect the main steel hull of the vessel.

When steel is placed in salt water, it behaves like part of an electrical battery. In any battery there are two electrodes (a negative electrode or cathode, and a positive electrode or anode). As the battery works, one of the electrodes (the positive electrode, or anode) is corroded (used up).

There is a danger that the steel of a ship's hull will behave as the electrode that is used up and cause severe corrosion to the ship. However, if pieces of aluminum are placed on the hull below the waterline, the aluminum is sacrificed instead, so protecting the hull.

Scientists call this effect "cathodic protection" because the hull of the ship is the cathode of the natural battery. It is far easier to replace chunks of aluminum bolted to the steel hull than to have to replace the whole hull! The secret to how this works lies in the fact that aluminum is much more reactive than iron. Other common cathodic protectors are zinc and magnesium.

corrosion: the *slow* decay of a substance resulting from contact with gases and liquids in the environment. The term is often applied to metals. Rust is the corrosion of iron.

oxide: a compound that includes oxygen and one other element.

rust: the corrosion of iron and steel.

siding: a surface sheet of material designed to protect other materials from corrosion.

▼ The hulls of ships are usually fitted with sacrificial anodes. As they are below the waterline, they are normally unseen except when the ship is in dry dock.

RICHARDS MEMORIAL LIBRARY
18 NORTH WASHINGTON STREET
NORTH ATTLEBORO. MA 02760

Anodizing aluminum

The word anodizing refers to a shiny protective coating that is often applied to aluminum to improve its looks. It is the opposite of the process of electroplating.

An anode is the electrode of a cell on which a substance oxidizes (corrodes). Anodizing is a process that uses electricity to produce this layer of oxide in a controlled way in order to protect a surface from further corrosion.

The anodizing process

Aluminum is placed in a chemical bath that will carry electricity, usually sulfuric or chromic acid. The aluminum acts as an anode. A cathode, often a carbon rod, is also placed in the bath. This makes an electrolytic cell. An electric current is passed through the cell, and the surface of the aluminum immediately begins to change. The acid liberates oxygen at the anode and this combines with the aluminum to make aluminum oxide.

In air aluminum would develop a very thin surface coating of oxide, but in anodized aluminum, the oxide is a far thicker protective coating. It is also possible to add color during this process. And because anodizing is a change to the surface of the metal, it does not chip or wear off as a paint or plastic coating might.

Anodized aluminum is used as a decorative form of aluminum on hi-fi and other electrical equipment. It is used for vehicle parts and can be used for both lighting and electrical fittings.

▼ These cowboy spurs are anodized so that they will not corrode even when used for long periods out in the rangelands.

anode: the negative terminal of a battery or the positive electrode of an electrolysis cell.

anodizing: a process that uses the effect of electrolysis to make a surface corrosion-resistant.

electrolysis: an electrical-chemical process that uses an electric current to cause the breakup of a compound and the movement of metal ions in a solution. The process happens in many natural situations (as for example in rusting) and is also commonly used in industry for purifying (refining) metals or for plating metal objects with a fine, even metal coating.

electroplating: depositing a thin layer of a metal onto the surface of another substance using electrolysis.

oxide: a compound that includes oxygen and one other element.

▲ There are two ways of providing a protective and decorative coating to aluminum products. The cheaper way is to apply a surface paint, but this is liable to wear off through handling. The better solution is to anodize the aluminum so that it remains protected and good-looking throughout the lifetime of the product.

◄ This saucepan is made from anodized aluminum. The aluminum oxide surface has the same hardness as other aluminum oxide minerals, such as sapphire, and so it is harder than stainless steel and even more scratch-resistant. By anodizing the surface, manufacturers can use aluminum (which is reknowned for its good heat transmission properties, but usually suffers from being too soft for prolonged use) for high-quality, long-lasting cookware.

Aluminum as a conductor

Aluminum is a good conductor of both heat and electricity. It has found widespread applications in the electricity supply industry and also in places where good heat conductivity is needed, such as in radiators and cookware.

An electrical conductor

Aluminum conducts electricity about two-thirds as well as copper. When made as a special alloy, or mixture of metals, aluminum is an even better conductor than copper on a weight-for-weight basis. This is because aluminum is only one-third as dense as copper. It is also very much cheaper to use than copper, especially where large cables are needed, such as those slung between pylons or the main cables buried beneath the street. Today more than nine out of every ten kilometers of large-diameter electrical cable are made from aluminum rather than traditional copper.

▶ Overhead cables are made of twisted strands of aluminum surrounding a steel cable core. The steel is used to give the cable strength. Aluminum cables are lighter and therefore require less substantial pylons than if copper were used.

▲ A section of underground cable, as would be used to supply the electricity to a street, shows three cores made from aluminum and insulated from each other by plastic coatings.

alloy: a mixture of a metal and various other elements.

density: the mass per unit volume (e.g., g/cc).

A heat conductor

Like all metals, aluminum conducts heat and so can be used either to carry heat away from a hot object or to bring heat to a cold object.

Aluminum is very much more expensive than steel; but where light weight is important, such as in aircraft, car or motorcycle engines, aluminum is often the preferred choice. It is nearly twice as good a conductor, weight for weight, as copper, and about nine times as good as steel.

Because aluminum can be cast into detailed shapes and is easy to cut, it is sometimes used for the whole of the main engine part (known as the engine block). It is also used in the radiators of most engines. Aluminum used to conduct heat can easily be seen in motorcycle engines, where the cooling fins show clearly.

◀ Aluminum is widely used for cooking utensils because of its good heat conductivity and light weight.

▲ Aluminum is used to carry heat away from sensitive electrical components on a circuit. The heating fins are light weight and so do not damage the board (as heavy steel might).

Aluminum as a reflector

One of the most useful features of aluminum is its excellent reflective properties.

Aluminum reflects about nine-tenths of heat reaching it. This means it can be used to reflect heat back inside a room or container to help keep it warm, or it can be used to reflect heat away from a container to keep it cool. For this reason aluminum is often used as part of the insulation of a house.

The reflective properties of aluminum can also be used in a quite different way. If an aircraft wants to jam the radar of an incoming missile, it can release large amounts of aluminum flakes or strips. These reflect the radar signals of the missile and make it impossible to detect the correct target.

▼ Aluminum is increasingly used to conserve energy both in home heating and cooling and in the transportation industry. Aluminum storm doors and windows, insulation backed with aluminum foil, and aluminum siding are excellent insulators.

Aluminum and reflection in space

Aluminum is an excellent material to use in spacecraft and even in life-support systems. This is because it is light, strong and has many useful heat-reflecting properties.

The space environment is very harsh. People in space suits can be overheated while they are directly in sunlight, but they can begin to freeze when they are in the shade.

Aluminum helps to prevent the extremes of heat gain and loss by reflecting the radiated heat away from the space suit and also reflecting the body heat back in. This keeps down the amount of heating or cooling equipment that has to be fitted onto the space suit.

▶ Space suits make extensive use of aluminum.

Aluminum is a poor "radiator"

One of the special features of aluminum is that it is very poor at radiating heat. This means that, for example, if the sun shines on a piece of aluminum, any heat energy not reflected will cause the aluminum to heat up, but very little of the heat will be released.

Aluminum shares its heat by conduction or by heating the surrounding air, so that heat is lost by convection.

This means that a sheet of aluminum used to protect an object from the Sun will be much more effective than a sheet of steel. The aluminum will absorb the heat, whereas the steel would absorb the heat on one side and radiate it from the other.

conduction: (i) the exchange of heat (heat conduction) by contact with another object or (ii) allowing the flow of electrons (electrical conduction).

convection: the exchange of heat energy with the surroundings produced by the flow of a fluid due to being heated or cooled.

radiation: the exchange of energy with the surroundings through the transmission of waves or particles of energy. Radiation is a form of energy transfer that can happen through space; no intervening medium is required (as would be the case for conduction and convection).

▼ Aluminum is often used instead of silver on large mirrors. It has good reflective properties but is far less expensive than silver. The mirrors shown here are part of a solar generating plant.

Aluminum containers

The food and drink industry is the world's biggest user of aluminum. Factories that make aluminum containers account for about one-third of the world demand for aluminum.

By far the greatest demand is for aluminum cans, which have replaced the more traditional tin-plated steel can. The softness of aluminum allows the cans to be pushed into shape (extruded), while the force needed to tear the aluminum by the ring-pull opener on drink cans is small because the aluminum has relatively little strength.

Modern packaging uses aluminum interleaved with plastic and paper to make other forms of cartons that can be sealed. This allows liquids to be kept for long periods without the need for refrigeration.

On a quite different scale, because aluminum resists attack by some acids, it can be used to transport and store them.

Cooking utensils

One of the first uses for aluminum was for cooking utensils, and many pans are still made from aluminum, either with or without nonstick coatings. High-quality utensils are hardened by anodizing (see page 26).

The food-processing industry uses aluminum for utensils such as steamers as well as for its packaging.

▲ ◄ Aluminum-lined containers reflect back the heat. This property is used to help to keep hot food hot and cold food cold.

Aluminum is also easy bent to shape, while the aluminum oxide surface does not react with food or become corroded.

extrusion: forming a shape by pushing it through a die. For example, toothpaste is extruded through the cap (die) of the toothpaste tube.

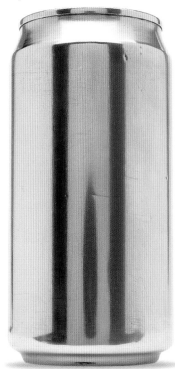

Contrasts in canning

A "tin can" is made from steel that has been coated with tin and sealed by soldering. The tin coating can be scratched away, allowing the steel to rust. Aluminum cans are lighter, do not rust, and can be extruded, thus removing the need for soldered seals. It is also easier to paint a decoration directly onto aluminum, so no more costly paper wrappers are used on steel cans.

▼▶ Aluminum can be made thin enough so that it can be torn. The special shapes on the top of many cans are designed to fail and produce a clean pouring opening. The lever arrangement on the can is to save the can pulls from being discarded and polluting the environment.

Aluminum and acid containers

Aluminum has the advantage of being resistant to attack by a variety of chemicals. Although it is readily corroded by most alkalis (which attack the surface oxide film), aluminum does not react with ammonia, and so it can be used to store and transport it.

Aluminum is far more resistant to neutral or acid solutions, in particular, acetic acid and concentrated nitric acid. For this reason many transport and storage containers for these chemicals are made from aluminum.

Aluminum oxide for separating mixtures

Aluminum oxide (alumina) is one of the most common yet overlooked of compounds.
It occurs in all of the world's soils, combining with silicon compounds to make tiny particles of clay. Clays are important to a soil because they can hold nutrients (ions) on their surfaces, so in general a fertile soil is a soil with clay.

The way that aluminum oxide acts as a filter can be demonstrated by pouring a mixture of dyes in solution through a tube containing aluminum oxide powder.

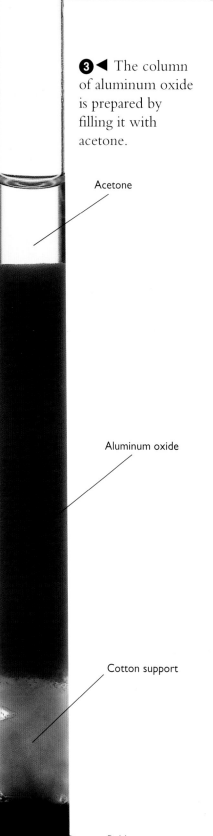

❸◀ The column of aluminum oxide is prepared by filling it with acetone.

Acetone

Aluminum oxide

Cotton support

Rubber stopper with hole

❶◀ Most organic substances are made of a variety of compounds. Beetroot is a good example. It is first prepared by crushing it using a pestle and mortar.

❷▶ The beetroot juice is diluted with a liquid in which it can dissolve (in this case acetone).

■ **acetone**: a petroleum-based solvent.

■ **dye**: a colored substance that will stick to another substance so that both appear colored.

■ **fertile**: able to provide the nutrients needed for unrestricted plant growth.

■ **nutrients**: soluble ions that are essential to life.

■ **organic substance**: a substance that contains carbon.

4 ◄ The beetroot juice is added to the top of the column.

The cotton is still colorless because none of the components of the beetroot juice have yet been washed through.

5 ► The first component of the beetroot juice emerges from the base of the tube. It is a yellow substance.

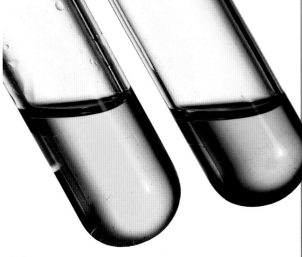

6 ▲ These are the first two components collected from the tube. Notice they are slightly different colors. The substance on the right is chlorophyll (the green pigment in plants), while that on the left is called xanthophyl.

Also...

The process demonstrated here is an example of chromatography, the use of a compound that does not react to separate the components of a complex substance (in this case a mixture of vegetable dyes). A substance like aluminum oxide, used in this way, is called a stationary phase. Substances easily attach to its surface (a process called adsorption) and are also easily washed off again. Each substance "sticks" to the aluminum oxide to a different degree, so that the least firmly stuck can be washed off most easily. The next one then washes off, and so on. As a result, the various compounds making up the original substance wash out of the base of the column one at a time and can be collected separately.

Aluminum sulfate (alum)

Alum is a compound of aluminum sulfate. It is used as a mordant, that is, a substance that will absorb dyes and so allow some natural fabrics to be colored. The dye-absorbing property of alum is shown here.

For many thousands of years, people knew that clay-rich rocks contained a useful substance, even though they could not extract it properly or find out what it was. So they called it the metal of clay. Alum was eventually obtained by heating suitable rocks, often clay-rich rocks called shales, in sulfuric acid.

Today alum is still used as a mordant to help fix dyes in cotton fabric. The fabrics are first dipped in a solution containing alum and then in a solution of alkali so that a precipitate of aluminum hydroxide (the real mordant) is formed between the fibers. As the cotton fabric dries, the tiny particles of aluminum hydroxide remain in the fabric, and the dye sticks to them. Alum is also used as a filler in paper and to purify water.

◄ Freshly precipitated aluminum hydroxide, a nearly colorless, gelatinous solid, shown here in a water suspension.

► A purple vegetable dye

EQUATION: Precipitating aluminum hydroxide mordant

Aluminum sulfate (alum) + ammonia solution + water ⇨ aluminum hydroxide + ammonium sulfate

$$Al_2(SO_4)_3(aq) \quad + \quad 6NH_3(aq) \quad + \quad 6H_2O(l) \quad ⇨ \quad 2Al(OH)_3(s) \quad + \quad 3(NH_4)_2SO_4(aq)$$

▲ A traditionally dyed cotton rug from Afghanistan.

dye: a colored substance that will stick to another substance so that both appear colored.

gelatinous: a term meaning made with water. Because a gelatinous precipitate is mostly water, it is of a similar density to water and will float or lie suspended in the liquid.

mordant: any chemical that allows dyes to stick to other substances.

suspension: tiny particles suspended in a liquid.

Mordants for dyeing

Dyes will not easily stick to some natural fabrics such as cotton. So the fabric has to be treated with a special chemical that attracts the fabric and also the dye.

Alum is a mordant, a material that will mix with water in a solution to produce a precipitate that sticks fast to cotton fabric dipped in it.

▼ The precipitate, with dye stuck to the surfaces of the particles, has completely settled, leaving only a colorless liquid above, clearly showing that the aluminum hydroxide formed from the alum is an effective mordant.

▶ A suspension of freshly precipitated aluminum hydroxide is added to the dye and thoroughly shaken.

Also...

Modern "fiber-active" dyes actually bond to the fabric. For this reason they have a wider application than the traditional mordant, especially in the dyeing of synthetics, where mordants will not work.

Aluminum compounds as foaming agents

Aluminum compounds can be used both as a source of carbon dioxide gas and a source of foam. Carbon dioxide gas can, in turn, be used to put out fires. For this reason such combinations were used to make liquid-type fire extinguishers for many years.

In the extinguisher the two reagents (the liquids that will react) are kept apart until the extinguisher is to be used. Then a knob on the extinguisher is struck, breaking the seal between the liquids and causing them to react.

The reaction produces a gelatinous precipitate of aluminum hydroxide and carbon dioxide gas. The gas cannot easily escape through this sticky liquid, and instead forms bubbles inside it. The result is a foam containing carbon dioxide that immediately squirts from the extinguisher nozzle. This has the effect of blanketing the fire with materials that will not burn, thus preventing oxygen from feeding the flames.

❶▶ Imagine this flask as the inside of a fire extinguisher. Two colorless liquids are kept separate and do not react. The lower one is concentrated sodium carbonate solution; the upper one concentrated aluminum sulfate solution.

EQUATION: Fire extinguishing

Aluminum sulfate + sodium carbonate + water ⇨ aluminum hydroxide + carbon dioxide + sodium sulfate

$$Al_2(SO_4)_3(aq) + 3Na_2CO_3(aq) + 3H_2O(l) \Rightarrow 2Al(OH)_3(s) + 3CO_2(g) + 3Na_2SO_4(aq)$$

foam: a substance that is sufficiently gelatinous to be able to contain bubbles of gas. The gas bulks up the substance, making it behave as though it were semirigid.

gelatinous: a term meaning made with water. Because a gelatinous precipitate is mostly water, it is of a similar density to water and will float or lie suspended in the liquid.

reagent: a starting material for a reaction.

▼ Carbon dioxide is used in fire extinguishers because it is not combustible. Surrounding a burning object with carbon dioxide therefore deprives the object of oxygen, and the fire goes out. Carbon dioxide is also a nonpolluting gas.

❷◄ Imagine that the fire extinguisher has been given a sharp tap to break the phial containing the aluminum sulfate solution, allowing it to mix with the sodium carbonate solution. The result is an immediate reaction, producing a gelatinous foam of carbon dioxide gas that froths up and does not disperse. These agents together make for an efficient fire-extinguishing combination.

Why recycling is vital

Aluminum is essential to many kinds of manufacturing, but making it from bauxite ore requires a great deal of expensive energy. In countries that refine aluminum, one-hundredth of all the electricity made in power stations may be used to run the refineries. It takes about 14 kilowatt-hours to refine each kilogram of alumina. (About the same as 14 single-bar electric heaters running for one hour.)

▲ Recycled aluminum cast into blocks.

But once aluminum has been refined and used, it can be melted down and recycled using just one-twentieth of the energy it took to make it in the first place. By saving this amount of energy, not only can resources like coal and oil be saved, but less carbon dioxide (a greenhouse gas) and sulfur and nitrogen oxides (acid rain gases) are released by power stations. For all these reasons it makes sense to recycle.

Recycling now accounts for about one-half of the total use of aluminum.

▲ A few cans thrown in a wastebasket may not seem very relevant to saving the world's aluminum resources...

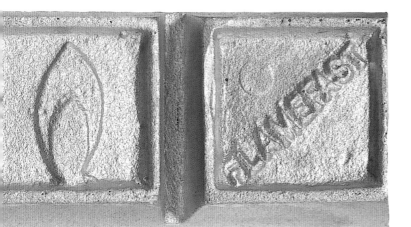

acid rain: rain that is contaminated by acid gases such as sulfur dioxide and nitrogen oxides released by pollution.

Greenhouse Effect: an increase in the global air temperature as a result of heat released from burning fossil fuels being absorbed by carbon dioxide in the atmosphere.

refining: separating a mixture into the simpler substances of which it is made. In the case of a rock, it means the extraction of the metal that is mixed up in the rock.

▲ … until you see the result of countrywide collections.

Aluminum and the environment

Aluminum is a very reactive element and therefore is normally found locked up as compounds. Most compounds are not at all harmful in the environment, and as in the case of clay minerals, they are positively important.

The only time that aluminum becomes a problem in the environment is as an indirect result of various pollutants that people create.

Of these the most serious by far is acid rain, which increases the acidity of water in the soil. If soils do not contain a buffer to cope with this onslaught, the soil may well become acid enough for aluminum to go into solution and find its way into water supplies for animals and plants. As aluminum is a toxic substance, the effects can be serious.

The other important environmental effect of aluminum occurs during mining. Aluminum occurs in surface sheets, and so its recovery destroys large areas of land. Most mines are found in the tropics, and many in tropical rainforests, where conditions are not favorable for the recovery of the land once it has been disturbed. Furthermore, only a small amount of the ore is transported to refineries; the majority, known as red mud, is often allowed to leave the mines, where it can pollute nearby streams and coasts. There are severe red-mud pollution problems in Jamaica, for example.

▶ Red mud from the chemical processing of bauxite can pollute rivers. In this picture from Jamaica it has been dammed in to form a dead lake.

▲ Gases and dust are collected in special hoods attached to each electrolytic cell.

acidity: a general term for the strength of an acid in a solution.

buffer: a chemistry term meaning a mixture of substances in solution that resists a change in the acidity or alkalinity of the solution.

clay: a microscopically small platelike mineral that makes up the bulk of many soils. It has a sticky feel when wet.

ion: an atom, or group of atoms, that has gained or lost one or more electrons and so developed an electrical charge.

pH: a measure of the hydrogen ion concentration in a liquid. Neutral is pH 7.0; numbers greater than this are alkaline, smaller numbers are acidic.

Aluminum and acid rain

Aluminum is insoluble if the pH of the soil is greater than 5. Only acid soils, such as podzols, which occur in areas of high rainfall or on acid parent materials, are therefore likely to cause aluminum to go into solution. So, under normal circumstances, aluminum compounds are not released into the soil or the water supply and are only taken up in small amounts by the body. More recently, the phenomenon of acid rain has changed this in some areas.

Acid rain occurs when polluting gases created by factories and vehicles mix with water vapor in the air and then eventually fall as acidic raindrops or snow. This extra acid gets into the soil where it begins to act on the abundant aluminum in the clay crystals.

Acid rain releases aluminum compounds, which can then be taken up by plant roots where they can damage or even kill plants.

The aluminum compounds also flow into nearby rivers and lakes, where they are absorbed by fish and other animals. Again the effects can be disastrous. In fact, many plants and animals die of aluminum poisoning. It is important to remember, though, that the real problem is not the presence of aluminum but the acid rain we produce by polluting the atmosphere with sulfur and nitrogen compounds.

Key facts about...

Aluminum

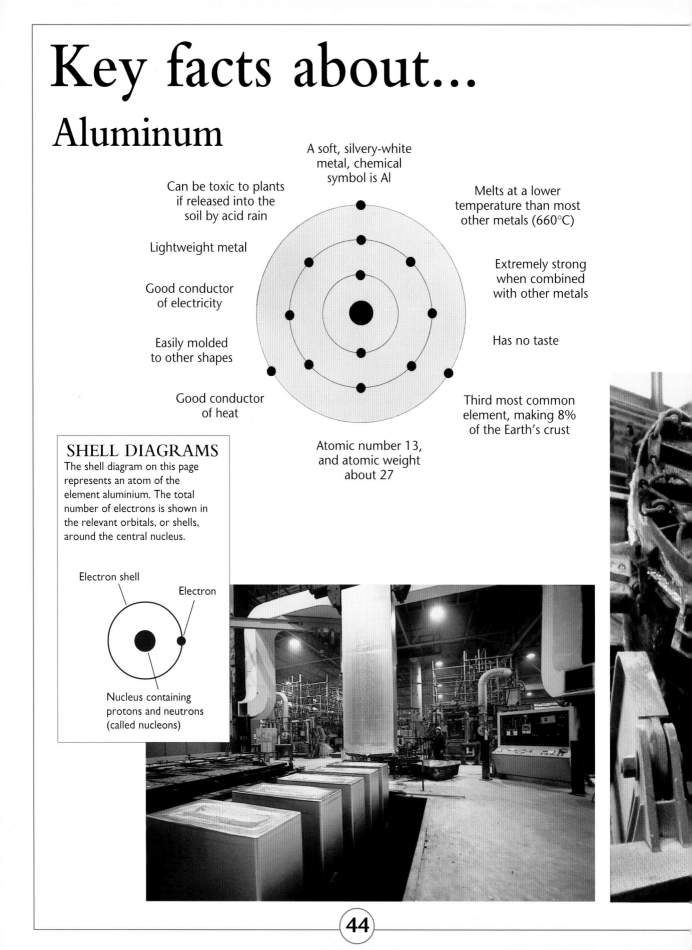

A soft, silvery-white metal, chemical symbol is Al

Can be toxic to plants if released into the soil by acid rain

Lightweight metal

Good conductor of electricity

Easily molded to other shapes

Good conductor of heat

Melts at a lower temperature than most other metals (660°C)

Extremely strong when combined with other metals

Has no taste

Third most common element, making 8% of the Earth's crust

Atomic number 13, and atomic weight about 27

SHELL DIAGRAMS

The shell diagram on this page represents an atom of the element aluminium. The total number of electrons is shown in the relevant orbitals, or shells, around the central nucleus.

Electron shell

Electron

Nucleus containing protons and neutrons (called nucleons)

► ▼ Molten aluminum is siphoned from the electrolytic cells (left) into a holding furnace where it is kept at 690 to 745°C for a two to three hours. Other elements can then be added to create the desired alloys. The resultant molten metal is then poured into molds of the desired ingot shape (below), from which aluminum products are manufactured. Careful control of the cooling of the aluminum produces a good internal structure to the metal casts (bottom left).

The Periodic Table

The Periodic Table sets out the relationships among the elements of the Universe. According to the Periodic Table, certain elements fall into groups. The pattern of these groups has, in the past, allowed scientists to predict elements that had not at that time been discovered. It can still be used today to predict the properties of unfamiliar elements.

The Periodic Table was first described by a Russian teacher, Dmitry Ivanovich Mendeleev, between 1869 and 1870. He was interested in writing a chemistry textbook and wanted to show his students that there were certain patterns in the elements that had been discovered. So he set out the elements (of which there were 57 at the time) according to their known properties. On the assumption that there was pattern to the elements, he left blank spaces where elements seemed to be missing. Using this first version of the Periodic Table, he was able to predict in detail the chemical and physical properties of elements that had not yet been discovered. Other scientists began to look for the missing elements, and they soon found them.

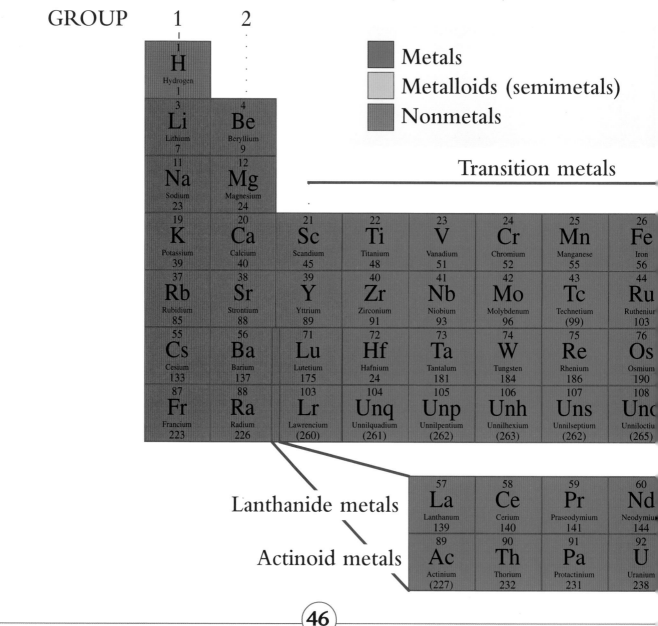

Hydrogen did not seem to fit into the table, and so he placed it in a box on its own. Otherwise the elements were all placed horizontally. When an element was reached with properties similar to the first one in the top row, a second row was started. By following this rule, similarities among the elements can be found by reading up and down. By reading across the rows, the elements progressively increase their atomic number. This number indicates the number of positively charged particles (protons) in the nucleus of each atom. This is also the number of negatively charged particles (electrons) in the atom.

The chemical properties of an element depend on the number of electrons in the outermost shell.

Atoms can form compounds by sharing electrons in their outermost shells. This explains why atoms with a full set of electrons (like helium, an inert gas) are unreactive, whereas atoms with an incomplete electron shell (such as chlorine) are very reactive. Elements can also combine by the complete transfer of electrons from metals to nonmetals, and the compounds formed contain ions.

Radioactive elements lose particles from their nucleus and electrons from their surrounding shells. As a result they change their atomic number and so become new elements.

Atomic (proton) number — 13 — Symbol
Al
Aluminum — Name
27 — Approximate relative atomic mass

3	4	5	6	7	0
					2 He Helium 4
5 B Boron 11	6 C Carbon 12	7 N Nitrogen 14	8 O Oxygen 16	9 F Fluorine 19	10 Ne Neon 20
13 Al Aluminum 27	14 Si Silicon 28	15 P Phosphorus 31	16 S Sulfur 32	17 Cl Chlorine 35	18 Ar Argon 40

27 Co Cobalt 59	28 Ni Nickel 59	29 Cu Copper 64	30 Zn Zinc 65	31 Ga Gallium 70	32 Ge Germanium 73	33 As Arsenic 75	34 Se Selenium 79	35 Br Bromine 80	36 Kr Krypton 84
45 Rh Rhodium 103	46 Pd Palladium 106	47 Ag Silver 108	48 Cd Cadmium 112	49 In Indium 115	50 Sn Tin 119	51 Sb Antimony 122	52 Te Tellurium 128	53 I Iodine 127	54 Xe Xenon 131
77 Ir Iridium 192	78 Pt Platinum 195	79 Au Gold 197	80 Hg Mercury 201	81 Tl Thallium 204	82 Pb Lead 207	83 Bi Bismuth 209	84 Po Polonium (209)	85 At Astatine (210)	86 Rn Radon (222)
109 Une nilennium (266)									

61 Pm omethium (145)	62 Sm Samarium 150	63 Eu Europium 152	64 Gd Gadolinium 157	65 Tb Terbium 159	66 Dy Dysprosium 163	67 Ho Holmium 165	68 Er Erbium 167	69 Tm Thulium 169	70 Yb Ytterbium 173
93 Np Neptunium (237)	94 Pu Plutonium (244)	95 Am Americium (243)	96 Cm Curium (247)	97 Bk Berkelium (247)	98 Cf Californium (251)	99 Es Einsteinium (252)	100 Fm Fermium (257)	101 Md Mendelevium (258)	102 No Nobelium (259)

Understanding equations

As you read through this book, you will notice that many pages contain equations using symbols. If you are not familiar with these symbols, read this page. Symbols make it easy for chemists to write out the reactions that are occurring in a way that allows a better understanding of the processes involved.

Symbols for the elements

The basis of the modern use of symbols for elements dates back to the 19th century. At this time a shorthand was developed using the first letter of the element wherever possible. Thus "O" stands for oxygen, "H" stands for hydrogen

and so on. However, if we were to use only the first letter, then there could be some confusion. For example, nitrogen and nickel would both use the symbols N. To overcome this problem, many elements are symbolized using the first two letters of their full name, and the second letter is not in capitals. Thus although nitrogen is N, nickel becomes Ni. Not all symbols come from the English name; many use the Latin name instead. This is why, for example, gold is not G but Au (for the Latin *aurum*) and sodium has the symbol Na, from the Latin *natrium*.

Compounds of elements are made by combining letters. Thus the molecule carbon

Written and symbolic equations

In this book important chemical equations are briefly stated in words (these are called word equations) and are then shown in their symbolic form along with the states.

What reaction the equation illustrates

Written equation

Symbol equation

EQUATION: The formation of calcium hydroxide

Calcium oxide + water ⇨ calcium hydroxide

$$CaO(s) \quad + \quad H_2O(l) \quad ⇨ \quad Ca(OH)_2(aq)$$

heated

Sometimes you will find an additional description below the symbolic equation.

Symbol showing the state:
s is for solid, l is for liquid,
g is for gas and aq is for aqueous.

Diagrams

Some of the equations are shown as graphic representations.

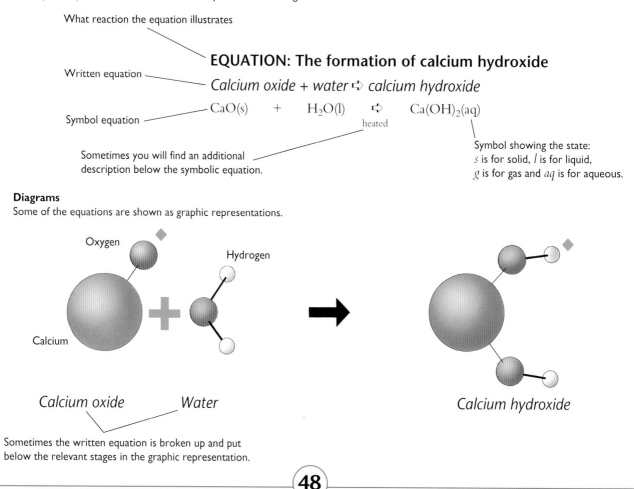

Oxygen

Hydrogen

Calcium

Calcium oxide   Water

Calcium hydroxide

Sometimes the written equation is broken up and put below the relevant stages in the graphic representation.

monoxide is CO. By using letters that are not capitals for the second letter of an element, it is possible to show that cobalt, symbol Co, is not the same as the molecule carbon monoxide, CO.

However, the letters can be made to do much more than this. In many molecules, atoms combine in unequal numbers. So, for example, carbon dioxide has one atom of carbon for every two of oxygen. This is shown by using the number 2 beside the oxygen, and the symbol becomes CO_2.

In practice, some groups of atoms combine as a unit with other substances. Thus, for example, calcium bicarbonate (one of the compounds used in some antacid pills) is written $Ca(HCO_3)_2$. This shows that the part of the substance inside the brackets reacts as a unit, and the "2" outside the brackets shows the presence of two such units.

Some substances attract water molecules to themselves. To show this a dot is used. Thus the blue-colored form of copper sulfate is written $CuSO_4.5H_2O$. In this case five molecules of water attract to one copper sulfate. When you

see the dot, you know that this water can be driven off by heating; it is part of the crystal structure.

In a reaction substances change by rearranging the combinations of atoms. The way they change is shown by using the chemical symbols, placing those that will react (the starting materials, or reactants) on the left and the products of the reaction on the right. Between the two, chemists use an arrow to show which way the reaction is occurring.

It is possible to describe a reaction in words. This gives a word equation. Word equations are used throughout this book. However, it is easier to understand what is happening by using an equation containing symbols. These are also given in many places. They are not used when the equations are very complex.

In any equation both sides balance; that is, there must be an equal number of like atoms on both sides of the arrow. When you try to write down reactions, you, too, must balance your equation; you cannot have a few atoms left over at the end!

The symbols in brackets are abbreviations for the physical state of each substance taking part, so that (*s*) is used for solid, (*l*) for liquid, (*g*) for gas and (*aq*) for an aqueous solution, that is, a solution of a substance dissolved in water.

Atoms and ions
Each sphere represents a particle of an element. A particle can be an atom or an ion. Each atom or ion is associated with other atoms or ions through bonds – forces of attraction. The size of the particles and the nature of the bonds can be extremely important in determining the nature of the reaction or the properties of the compound.

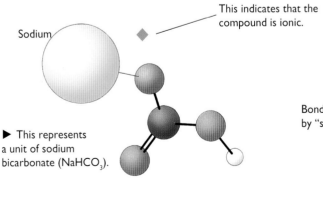

Sodium

This indicates that the compound is ionic.

▶ This represents a unit of sodium bicarbonate (NaHCO₃).

The term "unit" is sometimes used to simplify the representation of a combination of ions.

Chemical symbols, equations and diagrams
The arrangement of any molecule or compound can be shown in one of the two ways below, depending on which gives the clearer picture. The left-hand diagram is called a ball-and-stick diagram because it uses rods and spheres to show the structure of the material. This example shows water, H₂O. There are two hydrogen atoms and one oxygen atom.

Bond shown by "stick"

Colors too
The colors of each of the particles help differentiate the elements involved. The diagram can then be matched to the written and symbolic equation given with the diagram. In the case above, oxygen is red and hydrogen is gray.

Glossary of technical terms

acetone: a petroleum-based solvent.

acid rain: rain that is contaminated by acid gases such as sulfur dioxide and nitrogen oxides released by pollution.

acidity: a general term for the strength of an acid in a solution.

alloy: a mixture of a metal and various other elements.

amphoteric: a metal that will react with both acids and alkalis.

anode: the negative terminal of a battery or the positive electrode of an electrolysis cell.

anodizing: a process that uses the effect of electrolysis to make a surface corrosion-resistant.

bauxite: an ore of aluminum, of which about half is aluminum oxide.

bond: chemical bonding is either a transfer or sharing of electrons by two or more atoms. There are a number of types of chemical bond, some very strong (such as covalent bonds), others weak (such as hydrogen bonds). Chemical bonds form because the linked molecule is more stable than the unlinked atoms from which it formed. For example, the hydrogen molecule (H_2) is more stable than single atoms of hydrogen, which is why hydrogen gas is always found as molecules of two hydrogen atoms.

brazing: a form of soldering in which brass is used as the joining metal.

buffer: a chemistry term meaning a mixture of substances in solution that resists a change in the acidity or alkalinity of the solution.

clay: a microscopically small platelike mineral that makes up the bulk of many soils. It has a sticky feel when wet.

conduction: (i) the exchange of heat (heat conduction) by contact with another object or (ii) allowing the flow of electrons (electrical conduction).

convection: the exchange of heat energy with the surroundings produced by the flow of a fluid due to being heated or cooled.

corrosion: the *slow* decay of a substance resulting from contact with gases and liquids in the environment. The term is often applied to metals. Rust is the corrosion of iron.

crystal: a substance that has grown freely so that it can develop external faces. Compare with crystalline, where the atoms were not free to form individual crystals and amorphous, where the atoms are arranged irregularly.

density: the mass per unit volume (e.g., g/cc).

dissolve: to break down a substance in a solution without reacting.

dye: a colored substance that will stick to another substance so that both appear colored.

electrolysis: an electrical-chemical process that uses an electric current to cause the breakup of a compound and the movement of metal ions in a solution. The process happens in many natural situations (as for example in rusting) and is also commonly used in industry for purifying (refining) metals or for plating metal objects with a fine, even metal coating.

electroplating: depositing a thin layer of a metal onto the surface of another substance using electrolysis.

extrusion: forming a shape by pushing it through a die. For example, toothpaste is extruded through the cap (die) of the toothpaste tube.

feldspar: a mineral consisting of sheets of aluminum silicate. This is the mineral from which the clay in soils is made.

fertile: able to provide the nutrients needed for unrestricted plant growth.

foam: a substance that is sufficiently gelatinous to be able to contain bubbles of gas. The gas bulks up the substance, making it behave as though it were semirigid.

gelatinous: a term meaning made with water. Because a gelatinous precipitate is mostly water, it is of a similar density to water and will float or lie suspended in the liquid.

gemstones: a wide range of minerals valued by people, both as crystals (such as emerald) and as decorative stones (such as agate). There is no single chemical formula for a gemstone.

granite: an igneous rock with a high proportion of silica (usually over 65%). It has well-developed large crystals. The largest pink, gray or white crystals are of feldspar.

Greenhouse Effect: an increase in the global air temperature as a result of heat released from burning fossil fuels being absorbed by carbon dioxide in the atmosphere.

igneous rock: a rock that has solidified from molten rock, either volcanic lava on the Earth's surface or molten magma deep underground. In either case the rock develops a network of interlocking crystals.

ion: an atom, or group of atoms, that has gained or lost one or more electrons and so developed an electrical charge. Ions behave differently from electrically neutral atoms and molecules. They can move in an electric field, and they can also bind strongly to solvent molecules such as water. Positively charged ions are called cations; negatively charged ions are called anions. Ions carry electrical current through solutions.

molecule: a group of two or more atoms held together by chemical bonds.

mordant: any chemical that allows dyes to stick to other substances.

nutrients: soluble ions that are essential to life.

ore: a rock containing enough of a useful substance to make mining it worthwhile.

organic substance: a substance that contains carbon.

oxide: a compound that includes oxygen and one other element.

pH: a measure of the hydrogen ion concentration in a liquid. Neutral is pH 7.0; numbers greater than this are alkaline, smaller numbers are acidic.

radiation: the exchange of energy with the surroundings through the transmission of waves or particles of energy. Radiation is a form of energy transfer that can happen through space; no intervening medium is required (as would be the case for conduction and convection).

reagent: a starting material for a reaction.

reduction: the removal of oxygen from a substance.

refining: separating a mixture into the simpler substances of which it is made. In the case of a rock, it means the extraction of the metal that is mixed up in the rock. In the case of oil it means separating the fractions of which it is made.

rust: the corrosion of iron and steel.

siding: a surface sheet of material designed to protect other materials from corrosion.

soldering: joining together two pieces of metal using solder, an alloy with a low melting point.

solution: a mixture of a liquid and at least one other substance (e.g., saltwater). Mixtures can be separated by physical means, for example, by evaporation and cooling.

suspension: tiny particles suspended in a liquid.

welding: fusing two pieces of metal together using heat.

Master Index